In Level 0, **Step 1** is ideal for chi  beginning their synthetic phonics learning.

The letter sounds introduced in this book are:

g k e u h l j v w x y z qu

Special features:

Read this introduction to your child

It's the Underwater Kingdom! Can you help Emma find an underwater vehicle that has the letter sound u?

umbrella

sun

trunk

cup

puddle

u

plum

submarine

slug

12

13

Letter sound is in large, clear type

For the next part of her quest, Emma is at Jumping Jack's Playground.

Can you help her find two items of clothing that begin with the letter sound j?

jelly

jacket

j

jumper

jigsaw

juggler

jaguar

jewels

jelly beans

Jumping Jack

18

Pictures and labels help children practise the letter sound

Educational Consultant: Geraldine Taylor
Phonics and Book Banding Consultant: Kate Ruttle

LADYBIRD BOOKS

UK | USA | Canada | Ireland | Australia
India | New Zealand | South Africa

Ladybird Books is part of the Penguin Random House group of companies
whose addresses can be found at global.penguinrandomhouse.com.

www.penguin.co.uk www.puffin.co.uk www.ladybird.co.uk

First published 2020
001

Copyright © Ladybird Books Ltd, 2020

Printed in China

A CIP catalogue record for this book is available from the British Library

ISBN: 978-0-241-40518-5

All correspondence to
Ladybird Books
Penguin Random House Children's
80 Strand, London WC2R 0RL

Emma Explorer

Written by Catherine Baker
Illustrated by Michael Emmerson

Emma Explorer is on a quest. She wants to win the Letter Collector Medal!

Help Emma find five animals in Golden Garden that begin with the letter sound **g**.

guinea pig

goose

game

golfer

6

gorilla

girl

gate

goat

goldfish

Emma is in King Ken's kitchen.
What a lot of things begin with **k**!

Can you help Emma find the
biggest thing that begins with
the letter sound **k**?

koala

kitten

kangaroo

kennel

kite

key

King Ken

kiwi

ketchup

kettle

9

How exciting! Emma is exploring in the desert.

How many things can you see that begin with the letter sound **e**?

elbow

e

elf

engine

emerald

egg

elk

elephant

11

It's the Underwater Kingdom!
Can you help Emma find an underwater vehicle that has the letter sound u?

trunk

plum

slug

umbrella

sun

cup

pu**d**dle

s**u**bmarine

13

Emma has to go to Happy Hill
to find two plants that begin
with the letter sound **h**.

She thinks it will be hard –
but you can help her!

house

h

hen

hammock

helicopter

hot-air
balloon

horse

hippo

hedge

heather

15

Emma is at Lazy Lake.
She would like to rest here,
but there is lots to see!

Can you spot three sleepy
animals that begin with the
letter sound l?

lemur

lolly

lamb

lunchbox

leopard

lamp post

log

lifebelt

lake

17

For the next part of her quest, Emma is at Jumping Jack's Playground.

Can you help her find two items of clothing that begin with the letter sound j?

juggler

jumper

jewels

jelly

jacket

jaguar

jigsaw
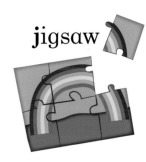

jelly beans

Jumping
Jack

Emma's voyage continues in the Violet Van. There are lots of things to see outside.

What musical instrument can you spot that begins with the letter sound v?

vet

vanilla ice-cream

van

vegetable garden

violin

volcano

village

21

It's turning chilly for Emma's next challenge.

Help her find some footwear that begins with the letter sound **w** in this Wonderful Winter Wonderland!

web

W

walking stick

wellington boots

wall

watch

wolf

well

windmill

walrus

23

Emma needs to visit the Fox's Island. This is a tricky challenge!

Can you spot a number with the letter sound **x**?

lyn**x**

si**x**

sa**x**ophone

pixie

ox

box

fox

axe

25

This challenge is fun! Emma has to find a toy that begins with the letter sound **y** on the Yellow Octopus pirate ship.

Can you help?

yolk

yoghurt

yacht

yak

yams

yoga

yawn

yo-yo

27

Emma has nearly finished her quest. But now she needs to be brave.

She has to go in the Zooming Rocket and find an animal that begins with the letter sound z! Can you see it?

zebra

zero

zip

zoo

zigzag

zap

Congratulations! You have helped Emma to win the Letter Collector Medal!

Can you spot a royal person beginning with the letter sound **qu**?

You are a great Letter Collector!

quarter

quill

For my parents and sisters
D.L.

For Felix Hilton
J.J.

Love and Best wishes
to Suzi from M. Leslie.
1987

First published 1985 by Walker Books Ltd,
184–192 Drummond Street, London NW1 3HP

Text © 1985 David Lloyd
Illustrations © 1985 Jane Johnson

First printed 1985
Printed and bound by L.E.G.O., Vicenza, Italy

British Library Cataloguing in Publication Data
Lloyd, David, *1945*–
Pirates. – (Let's pretend)
I. Title II. Johnson, Jane III. Series
823′.914[J] PZ7
ISBN 0-7445-0243-8

PIRATES

Written by David Lloyd
Illustrated by Jane Johnson

WALKER BOOKS
LONDON

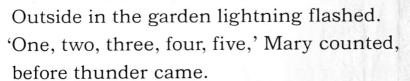

Outside in the garden lightning flashed.
'One, two, three, four, five,' Mary counted,
before thunder came.
'Let's pretend to be sailors in a storm,'
William said.
They all went on board the boat.

'The wind is very wild,' Mary said.
'The waves are very loud,' William said.

'This is dangerous,' Lucy said,
'and I'm brave.'

'I'm Captain Thunder,' William said,
'a pirate from the China Sea.'
'I'm a kidnapped queen,' Mary said,
'and Lucy is my maid.'

'No, I'm a pirate too, and my
name is Lucy,' Lucy said.

'Look! Coming across the sea!
A shipwrecked cat!' William said.
'It's Tabitha,' Lucy said.
'I'll have to rescue her. I think she's
frightened of the storm,' Mary said.

Mary plunged into the sea. She picked up
Tabitha and brought her back to the boat.

'Well done, prisoner,' William said.
'It's all right, Tabby,' said Lucy.

At the very darkest, loudest part of the storm,
everyone lay down on the deck.

'The sails are splitting,'
William said.
'The mast is cracking,' Mary said.
'I don't like this,' Lucy said,
holding on to Tabitha.

'Land ahoy!' shouted William when at last the sea grew calm again.

Everyone went ashore.

'You brought me home,' Mary said.
'You're kind pirates really.'

Tabitha walked away.

Mary, William and Lucy
went to look out of the window.

There were puddles in the garden
and the sun was shining.
Dark clouds showed which way
the storm had gone.

'Let's go outside now,' Lucy said.